Fosdyke Saga Two

60p

Fosdyke Saga Two

More of the famous DAILY MIRROR strip

By BILL TIDY

WOLFE PUBLISHING LIMITED
10 EARLHAM STREET ● LONDON WC2H 9LP

SBN 7234 0529 8

Printed by C. Nicholls & Company Ltd
The Philips Park Press
Manchester
M11 4AU

Fosdyke Saga Two

Scattered throughout the world, the intrepid Fosdykes, rulers of a mighty empire, risk life and limb to spread the gospel of tripe. In Chicago, Tom Fosdyke has smashed the alcoholic tripe racket run by the iniquitous Ditchley, the hate-crazed villain whose sole aim is to destroy the inheritors of his father's business.

A few days later . . .

SOUTH AMERICA IS A HUNGRY CONTINENT AND THE IDEAL PLACE FOR FOSDYKES TO TAKE ROOT IS...

F90

..THE REPUBLIC OF CHILI GUAY. I'LL NOT MESS ABOUT WITH MINOR OFFICIALS. I'LL GO STRAIGHT TO THE TOP.. AND THAT'S THE MAN I WANT!

EL PRESIDENTE RAMIREZ

WHERE CAN I FIND THE PRESIDENT?

BEHIND THAT SHED, SENOR!

EL PRESIDENTE RAMIREZ

OH.. THAT'S A BAD START. NOW I'LL HAVE TO FIND THE NEW PRESIDENT.

PRESIDENTE REZ

F91

EXCUSE ME. WHO IS THE CURRENT PRESIDENT OF CHILIGUAY?

MORALES. HE TOOK OFFICE TEN MINUTES AGO.

AH, NOW WE'RE GETTING SOMEWHERE. COULD YOU DIRECT ME TO HIS PALACE?

SI SENOR. AS A MATTER OF FACT WE'RE GOING THAT WAY OURSELVES!

Meanwhile far away in the Sahara, Albert Fosdyke, contestant in the Manchester to India air race, finds himself best man at the wedding of the Hon. Cynthia Spofforth and Omar the Terrible, and the reluctant possessor of Omar's 45 previous wives . . .

And after the ceremony . . .

But Albert's problems still abound . . .

And so the happy bachelor escapes . . .

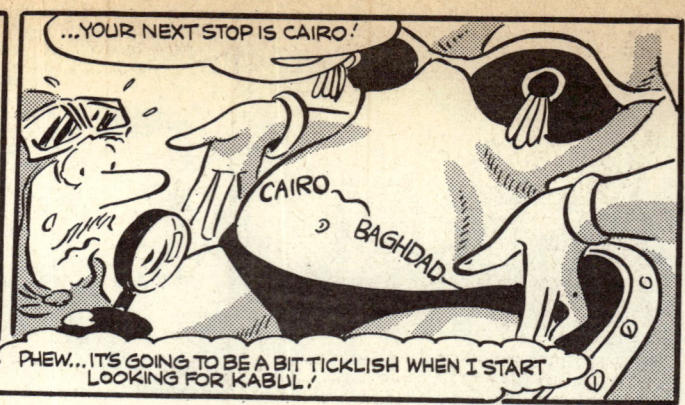

And in a Moscow fortress Sir Jos Fosdyke fights for his honour in the passionate embrace of brutal General Blaskova, head of the dreaded Secret Tripe Police . . .

But next morning Sir Jos is still in fighting spirit . . .

The farcical trial begins . . .

Tortured by regrets, the helpless victim of Soviet injustice passes a restless night, until . . .

And some
hours later . . .

Meanwhile the Chiliguayan branch of the Fosdyke empire makes little progress . . .

In Cairo Albert encounters his latest rival in the air race . . .

And as Albert wings his way over the sandy wastes . . .

While many miles away another feat of aerial daring is enacted . . .

And so our hero returns to Manchester . . .

And as the days pass Monti continues to evade Sir Jos's challenge . . .

Languishing in a Chiliguayan prison, the ex-Minister of Tripe muses on the latest cruel turn of Fortune's wheel . . .

While Albert grapples gamely with the desert sand . . .

In Manchester Jos finally gets to grips with his daughter's slippery admirer . . .

NOW LOOK HERE, HOUDINI. IF YOU HAVE HOPES OF BEIN' MY SON-IN-LAW, YOU'LL HAVE TO SHAKE YOURSELF.
TIMES ARE HARD FOR ILLUSIONISTS, SIR JOS. ENGAGEMENTS ARE HARD TO—
WELL, HERE'S A NOVEL IDEA! WHY DON'T YOU GO DOWN TO THAT PLACE WHERE THEY OFFER PEOPLE JOBS. IT'S CALLED—
I KNOW WHAT IT'S CALLED. I WAS THERE LAST WEEK WORKING ON A TRICK.
WHAT TRICK?
THE DISAPPEARING LABOUR EXCHANGE TRICK.
F143

FATHER, YOU'VE BEEN AT MONTI AGAIN!
SORRY, VICKY, BUT HE'S IDLE!
HE'S NOT. WE'RE LEAVING FOR AN ENGAGEMENT AT SALFORD CEMETERY. HE'S ATTEMPTING THE FANTASTICALLY DANGEROUS BURIED COFFIN ESCAPE!
BY GUM, SHE'S INFATUATED. HE'LL ESCAPE FROM THAT COFFIN AND SHE'LL THINK HE'S THE GREATEST THING SINCE SLICED TRIPE!
YOU NEVER KNOW, THOUGH... WE MIGHT BE IN LUCK!
F144

At the cemetery . . .

F.145

F146

Meanwhile, in the Chiliguayan tripe tub . . .

MADE IT, BUT THIS BAMBOO IS SLIPPERY... CAN'T HOLD ON...

I'M SLIDING BACK INTO THE... AAH!

HA, FOSDYKE, THESE MIGHTY JAWS ARE GAPING WIDE!

BLAST YOU FOSDYKE! DAMN, HOW DO I GET THIS THING INTO REVERSE?

F149

THIS COULD GO ON ALL DAY, PRESIDENTE. HAVE YOU DECIDED WHICH ONE YOU WISH TO KEEP?

I'M TIRED OF THEM BOTH, PEDRO...

...ASSEMBLE A FIRING SQUAD AND TELL THAT PEASANT PIG TO OPERATE THE LIFTING MECHANISM.

F150

SHOOT THEM DOWN WHEN IT SLOWS!

Some hours later . . .

Swathed in bandages, Albert lies at the mercy of the lunatic egyptologist

But salvation is at hand . . .

And Monti the illusionist remains firmly ensconced in the Fosdyke home

But as the days go by . . .

F163

The following day . . .

Meanwhile, deep in the South American jungle, Tom and Ditchley take arms against a monstrous regiment of women . . .

Shortly afterwards . . .

Free once more, Albert makes for Baghdad . . .

Meanwhile, Canal Street, Manchester, bears witness to a deed of superhuman courage . . .

And later, at the hospital . . .

F183

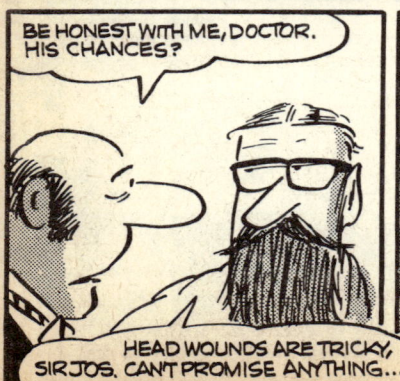

F184

In the distant jungle, can Ditchley, vanquisher of female hearts, captivate the mighty Queen of the Jivaros?

F185

And sixteen courses later . . .

YOU ARE INDEED JANGO, THE TRIPE GOD. THAT WAS TRIPE AT ITS SUBTLEST.

SIT BACK AND RELAX. HAVE YOU A MACHETE HANDY? I'D LIKE TO KILL DITCHLEY

FOSDYKE - YOU'RE JOKING!

NO! GIVE ME A CHANCE, I'LL CHANGE MY WAYS!

YOU'LL NEVER CHANGE YOU CUR. DON'T MAKE SO MUCH NOISE...

...THAT WAS 'MICKEY FINN' KNOCKOUT TRIPE I GAVE THEM. GET GOING!

F190

ZZZZZZ

ZZZZZ Z

Meanwhile, among the enemy-infested hills of the North West Frontier . . .

PAIN IN LEG UNBEARABLE... ABOUT TO FAINT... FAINTING... 10, 9, 8, 7....

HANG ON, CARRUTHERS, WE'LL BE TOUCHING DOWN AT KABUL IN MINUTES!

And in the oriental magnificence of a nearby rocky encampment . . .

But in a Manchester Hospital . . .

But some days later . . .

And as the terrible Jivaros lie locked in tripe-drugged slumber . . .

So the two sworn foes set out on an impossible journey . . .

F204

F.205

Meanwhile, on the polo field of Kabul . . .

A few minutes later . . .

THEY ARE ALL TAKEN, GREAT KHAN.

NOW LOOK HERE, YOU'VE WON THIS ONE BUT WE'LL GET YOU IN THE END.

WHY DON'T YOU SIGN UP WITH THE EMPIRE? WE'LL GIVE YOU SCHOOLS AND HOSPITALS. TEACH YOU —

I AM EAGER TO LEARN, GENERAL. TELL ME ABOUT POLO.

GOOD MAN! WELL, FOUR IN A TEAM, NO OFFSIDE, FAST GALLOPING GAME, SIX CHUKKAS OF 7½ MINUTES DURATION —

FZ13

MY WAZILS CHALLENGE YOU TO A GAME... FOR YOUR LIVES!

YOUR RABBLE CHALLENGE LIGHTFOOT'S HORSE! HARDLY A MATCH, OLD BOY. WE'D MURDER YOU. DOESN'T SEEM FAIR TO ME.

YOU WILL BE PLAYING FOR YOUR LIVES, GENERAL!

YES, BUT I DON'T LIKE TAKING ADVANTAGE OF ANYONE. I SAY! PERHAPS WE COULD GIVE YOU FIVE GOALS START!

VERY GENEROUS BUT I HAVE A BETTER IDEA...

FZ14

...YOUR TEAM WILL PLAY ON FOOT!

And on the ill-famed Devil's Island . . .

THIS IS A MISTAKE, COLONEL. WE ARE NOT THE MEN YOU ARE LOOKING FOR—

BUT OF COURSE, M'SIEU. YOU ARE INNOCENT, EH? EVERYONE ON DEVIL'S ISLAND IS INNOCENT.

THAT MAN LAYING WITH MADAME GUILLOTINE IS ALSO INNOCENT. VERY WELL, PASS ME THAT FILE...

JE SUIS INNOCENT!

F215

CHUNK!

...I WILL REVIEW HIS CASE THIS VERY MOMENT.

NOW THAT WE 'AVE ESTABLISHED THE INNOCENCE OF EVERY MAN ON DEVIL'S ISLAND, I WILL ASSIGN YOU TO WORK. NAMES?

ROGER DITCHLEY, DAM' YOU.

TOM FOSDYKE.

YOU WILL WORK ON THE SWAMP CLEARANCE CHAIN GANG.

I CAN COOK.

SO CAN I! MIRACLES WITH TRIPE AND PIGS FEET.

HA! INTERESTING. LET ME SEE WHAT YOU CAN DO.

F216

Five minutes later . . .

THANK GOD, IT JUST CAME TO THE BOIL BEFORE THE RANGE SANK IN THE SWAMP. IF HE LIKES THIS WE'LL BE PULLED TO SAFETY...

...IF HE DOESN'T LIKE IT...

HOW IS IT?

TELL US, MAN, TELL US!

F219

ATHEISTS! THE PADRE HAS NOT YET SAID GRACE!

BLAST HIM FOR A SLOW EATER, FOSDYKE... I'M GOING UNDER...

I 'AVE NEVAIR TASTED A PIG'S FEET DEVIL'S ISLAND WITH SAUCE TROTTAIR LIKE THAT. C'EST MAGNIFIQUE!

C'MON YOU TWO. LE FROT ISN'T GOING TO LIKE THIS!

PULL THEM OUT, 7396442. THEY WILL REPLACE TRIPLE AXE MURDERER LE FROT AS CAMP CHEFS. HE WILL WORK UNDER THEM.

F220

While in the silenced Fosdyke tripe works . . .

And after some weeks of dynamic activity . . .

So the historic First Tripiad is inaugurated . . .

...GO!

CCCP
PERU
ICELAND
SUOMI
TIBET

THAT CONCLUDES THE ELIMINATING HEATS, LUV. NOW WE'VE GOT THE THREE BEST TRIPE MEN IN THE WORLD TO FIGHT IT OUT. OUR OWN HAROLD OCKERBY...

GB

..OTTO FLEISPECK OF GERMANY, A TWENTY-FOOT POLE VAULTER, AND...

..CARLO TROPPOBELLI OF ITALY, THE WORLD'S FASTEST HURDLER.

ITALY

F 227

IT'S JUST OCKERBY, FLEISPECK, AND TROPPOBELLI NOW LUV. OUR LAD'S GOT A FIGHT ON HIS HANDS...

FOSDYKE'S TRIPE CONTEST

So to the last, fantastic day of the games . . .

Meanwhile, at the outpost of the Empire begins a life and death struggle . . .

But some hours later . . .

And on Devil's Island . . .

High on Everest's mantled slopes, a shadowy form struggles to safety . . .

Later, in the comfort of the expedition's tent . . .

Some shoulder-cracking hours later . . .

In Manchester the Fosdykes bask
in their recovered affluence.

Later that night . . .

Next day at the works . . .

YOU'LL BE PERFORMING THE NUPTIALS IN THE TRIPE SHED, VICAR. SYMBOLIC DON'T YOU THINK?

...ER...

WE'LL HAVE THE ORGAN OVER THERE, AND A CHOIR OF TWO HUNDRED APPRENTICE BLACK PUDDING SKINNERS BY THE SCALDING ROOM...

.. AND DON'T FORGET IT'S A BIT DAMP IN HERE, SO BRING YOUR WELLINGTONS ON THE BIG DAY.

F255

BY GUM, IT'S GOING TO BE A BIG AFFAIR, LUV. I'VE JUST ORDERED TWO DOZEN BRIDESMAIDS FROM THE LABOUR EXCHANGE.

I WISH THEY'D HAD A LONGER ENGAGEMENT. YOU KNOW HOW PEOPLE TALK ABOUT QUICK MARRIAGES.

LET 'EM TALK.. I JUST WANT OUR VICKY TO BE RADIANT AT A REAL POSH WEDDING!

YOU'RE RIGHT, JOS. OH, THE INVITATIONS. HOW MANY GUESTS ARE COMING?

DUNNO YET, LUV. IT DEPENDS ON HOW MUCH TRIPE WE SELL.

FREE WEDDING INVITATION WITH EVERY POUND OF FOSDYKE'S TRI

F256

And for Albert, victory is in sight . . .

Panel 1: LAST FEW MILES OF THE RACE. IT'S A MIRACLE THAT I'VE GOT THIS FAR!

Panel 2: LOTS OF ACTIVITY ON THE FIELD. RAJAHS, OFFICIALS.. SURELY I'M NOT THE FIRST ONE TO ARRIVE?

HAVE I WON? FIRST THINGS FIRST. TELEGRAPH THE FOLKS OF MY SAFE ARRIVAL. AH, THERE ARE MY TAXI-ING INSTRUCTIONS!

FOLLOW ME

F257

WHAT BAD LUCK TO PRANG RIGHT AT THE END OF THE RACE – HULLO! BETTER BE OFF. I SMELL SMOKE!

SAHIB!

THE VICEROY AND RAJAH OF BLAT BOTH CONGRATULATE YOU ON YOUR GREAT VICTORY, OH YES, INDEED!

IT'S OFFICIAL. I'VE WON! NOW LETS GET OUT OF HERE BEFORE –

OH DEAR ME, NO SIR! YOU MUST WAIT FOR COCKPIT PRESENTATION OF WINNERS CHEQUE!

F258

F 259

F260

Victoria's wedding day dawns . . .

But four hours later . . .

After days of
anguish . . .

At Liverpool dock . . .

Back home, Jos primes his youngest son for a dazzling career . . .

And so the youngest
Fosdyke enters the tripe-selling
lists . . .

But danger threatens at once . . .

Meanwhile, three
desperate men toss
upon the mighty
deep . . .

F27

F276

F277

Tom regains
consciousness on a
tranquil shore . . .

And while the castaway prays for rescue, a revived Victoria enjoys her heart-healing cruise . . .

So the rescue boat brings Tom to an unexpected reunion

As the ship leaves the Indian shore . . .

And back home at last . . .

Next day . . .

But in London . . .

And aboard the luxury liner . . .

A few hours later . . .

Meanwhile, outside Salford Museum . . .

And after many hours . . .

G5

TREASURES OF HUTUNKHAMEN EXH

NEARLY THERE, DAD, MY SPEED DUEL WITH BARON MIKIMOTO LOOMS.

HE DID SOME GOOD TIMES IN PRACTICE, LAD. ROUND THE EXHIBITION IN TWO MINUTES...

I DON'T WANT ANY LAST MINUTE PANICS, ALBERT. YOU HAVEN'T FORGOTTEN OWT?

DON'T THINK SO. I'VE OILED MY SKATES— OH NO!

ILLUSTRATED BROCHURE 3d

QUICK, DAD. SOME SMALL CHANGE!

BLAST! I LOST 20 YARDS BUYING THAT BROCHURE.

G6

THE JAP'S LEADING AT 'MUMMIFIED CATS CORNER' BUT ALBERT'LL PASS HIM..

...ON THE PHARAOH'S PYRAMID FOR HIS FAVOURITE GOLDFISH.

And what of young Tim in the hostile back streets of whelk-ridden London?

Panel 1:

I'M FINE, DAD... A FEW CUTS AND BRUISES —

GOOD LAD, TIM. HOW'S BUSINESS?

TERRIBLE. THEY SMASH MY BARROWS AS SOON AS I PUT THEM ON THE STREETS. IT'S HOPELESS.

Panel 2:

WHO'S 'THEY', LAD? F301

BIG ARTHUR'S LONDON GANG. HE'S THE WHELK CZAR, AND HE HATES COMPETITION.

Panel 3:

HELP ME PACK, BECKY. I'M CATCHING THE 12·30 TO EUSTON.

NO, JOS! NOT ANOTHER TRIPE WAR!

JOS, IF YOU GO, I'LL LEAVE YOU!

Panel 4:

I MEAN IT, JOS. IF YOU GO TO LONDON AND GET MIXED UP IN ANOTHER TRIPE WAR, I'M WALKING OUT ON YOU.

I'M SICK OF THE FIGHTING AND PAIN, THE WIDOWS AND ORPHANS.

Panel 5:

I MUST GO, BECKY. SPREADING TRIPE ACROSS THE GLOBE IS MY LIFE. I OWE IT TO OLD BEN DITCHLEY. A MAN MUST DO WHAT HE BELIEVES TO BE RIGHT...

..YOU MUST DO THE SAME, BECKY, BUT IF YOU DO WALK OUT ON ME, REMEMBER ONE THING...

Panel 6:

I'VE GOT ALL THE SUITCASES! F302

But the situation is already desperate . . .

Back in Fosdyke's London office . . .

I DIDN'T BELIEVE THAT STUFF ABOUT THE ROYAL FAMILY BEIN' AWAY, DAD. THEY WERE IN THE PALACE!

AYE, TIM, I SAW CURTAINS MOVE 'AS WE LEFT.

WE DON'T NEED HELP FROM THEM. I'LL HAVE THESE COCKNEYS GOBBLIN' TRIPE IN NO TIME.

GOSH, DAD, LOOK AT THIS!

G.10

LONDON WINKLE GANGS ROAM THE NORTH! IT'S CIVIL WAR!

FOSDYKE (LONDON)

WHELK REPRISALS IN BLACKPOOL

JELLIED EELS ATROCITY IN WIGAN

MANCUNIAN WINKLED TO DEATH

BY GUM, DAD, YOU'VE STARTED SUMMAT NOW. BIG ARFER'S MOB ARE TAKING REPRISALS BACK HOME!

EVENING TRUMPET

HAIL OF WHELKS STUNS MAYOR OF LIV

WE MUST GIVE UP OUR TRIPE ASSAULT HERE IN LONDON!

FACE FACTS. WE HAVEN'T SOLD AN OUNCE SINCE WE'VE BEEN HERE. FORGET IT, DAD...

THEY JUST DON'T LIKE TRIPE DOWN HERE!

DAD!

G.11

As Tim escorts his stricken parent back to friendlier climes . . .

But meanwhile Sir Jos sinks fast . . .

And on board ship . . .

At the bedside . . .

So the Fosdyke-Ditchley struggle reaches a crescendo.

And Alberts personal duel continues . . .

The hour for Tom's fight
with Ditchley is at hand . . .

TOM, LET ME FIGHT DITCHLEY. I'M YOUNGER AND I'VE PLAYED AGAINST THE ALL BLACKS

NO TIM, IT'S MY RESPONSIBILITY...

DITCHLEY'S PLAGUED US FOR YEARS. THE TIME HAS COME TO SETTLE HIS HASH ONCE AND FOR ALL.

NOT SO LOUD, TOM, YOU'LL WAKEN DAD—HULLO, HE'S COMIN' ROUND. DAD!

G28

STAY IN BED. YOU'VE GOT TRIPOPHOBIA!

I HEARD YOU TALKIN'. I'LL FIGHT DITCHLEY!

WHERE IS HE? I'LL BATTER HIM TO—

STOP HIM, TOM, HE'S RAVING!

G29

LOOK HERE, LADS, I'M THE TRIPE FATHER OF THIS FAMILY. WHAT I SAY IS LAW!

I'M A BIT SHAKY BUT I CAN STILL HANDLE DITCHLEY.

WHAT THE — OLD FOSDYKE INSTEAD OF TOM?

FOSDYKE'S DELICIOUS TRI

GET 'EM UP. I'M READY TO FIGHT FOR MY ENTIRE TRIPE EMPIRE!

But after the fight . . .

GIVE SIR JOS FIFTY THREE OF THESE PILLS EVERY NINE MINUTES.

G34

YOU'RE THE UMPTEENTH DOCTOR WE'VE HAD IN FOR JOS...

.. AND HIS TRIPOPHOBIA IS GETTING WORSE. I'M FED UP WITH YOU QUACKS.

MADAM, I RESENT—

ENOUGH TIME'S BEEN WASTED. THERE'S ONLY ONE PERSON WHO CAN SAVE MY JOS!

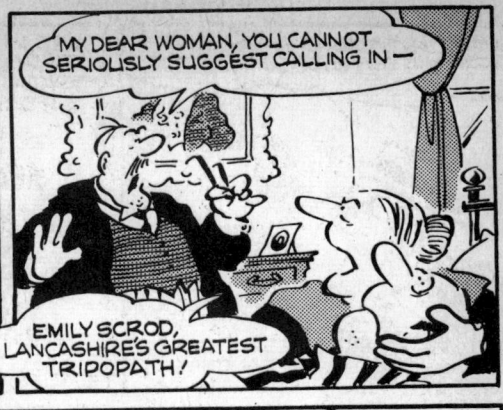

MY DEAR WOMAN, YOU CANNOT SERIOUSLY SUGGEST CALLING IN —

EMILY SCROD, LANCASHIRE'S GREATEST TRIPOPATH!

MADAM, THE MEDICAL PROFESSION DOES NOT RECOGNISE TRIPOPATHS. MRS SCROD IS A CHARLATAN, A FAKE!

WHAT HAVE YOU DONE FOR JOS? EACH DAY HIS KNEES GET SOFTER, HIS EARS DROOP...

I'M NOT STANDING BY TILL JOS FADES AWAY. I'M CALLING IN EMILY SCROD!

YOU ARE ACTING LIKE A TYPICALLY FOOLISH, HYSTERICAL WOMAN, BUT IF THAT IS YOUR LAST WORD...

.. ON YOUR OWN HEAD BE IT!

G35

And later that day . . .

EMILY SCROD'S HEALING MAGIC CAN SAVE YOUR FATHER'S LIFE. I WANT HER FOUND!

SHE WAS LAST HEARD OF LIVING DOWN A GRID IN BOLTON

SHE MAY HAVE MOVED ON SINCE THEN, SO...

..WE MUST ADVERTISE FOR HER...

.. AND WE'LL START RIGHT NOW!

WANTED E. SCROD

G36

So the country-wide search begins . . .

IS EVERYONE OUT LOOKING FOR EMILY SCROD?

ALL EXCEPT ALBERT. HE'D ALREADY STARTED ON HIS LATEST SPEED DUEL WITH BARON MIKIMOTO...

THEY'RE SEEING WHO CAN PUSH A CUCUMBER UP BLACKPOOL TOWER FASTEST WITH THEIR NOSES. HE PROMISED TO KEEP AN EYE OPEN FOR HER.

HOW CAN HE FOOL ABOUT WHEN WE'RE LOOKING FOR THE WOMAN WHO CAN CURE JOS'S TRIPOPHOBIA!

But on Blackpool Tower . . .

And back home again . . .

.. AND THE STACKS MUST DROP IN A STRAIGHT LINE WI' MINIMUM SOOTFALL. OH, AND ONE OTHER THING...

... THERE'S A ONE MINUTE TIME PENALTY...

... IF YOU BREAK THE EGGS!

A TIME PENALTY IF THE EGGS IN THE NEST AT THE TOP OF THE STACK SMASH WHEN IT FALLS. GO GENTLY, LAD.

G43

THE BARON'S 27 BRICKS AHEAD, BUT MY CHIMNEY IS QUIVERING...

... NOW ROUND TO THE OTHER SIDE FOR THE DECISIVE SWING!

BY GUM! BOTH 'TOPPLIN' IN RECORD TIME.

I MUST SAVE THE EGGS!

G44

WE'RE LEVEL WITH 20 YARDS TO GO. UNLESS THE BARON'S GOT ANYTHING UP HIS SLEEVE, IT'S GOING TO BE A DEAD·HEAT!

CLOSE THING LAD, BUT I'LL HAVE TO GIVE IT TO BARON THINGYBOB FOR STYLE AND INGENUITY...

...HE'S GOT EGG AND CHIPS IN HIS NEST!

G45

Meanwhile, bloody but unbowed, the evil Ditchley lurks in a nearby alehouse.

'ULLO ROGER! I HEAR OLD MAN FOSDYKE LAID YOU OUT, AND 'IM 'ARF DEAD WI' TRIPOPHOBIA. TUT, TUT!

SHUT YOUR MOUTH!

GOD KNOWS WHAT HE'LL DO TO YOU WHEN HE GETS BETTER!

NO CHANCE. HE'LL BE DEAD IN A WEEK.

DON'T BANK ON IT, THEY'VE CALLED IN LANCASHIRE'S MOST ILLUSTRIOUS TRIPOPATH TO FIX HIM...

And while the Fosdykes wait anxiously

So, some time later . . .

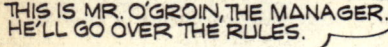

A few days later Sir Jos, fully recovered from his illness, is back in business . . .

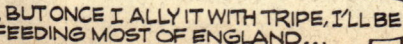

But Liverpool will not yield up its secret . . .

Meanwhile Albert and the Baron confer . . .

Once more the conquering
hero rejoins his family . . .

While in a sleazy
Liverpool lodging
house . . .

As the victorious Ditchley prances away . . .

In Manchester Baron
Mikimoto seeks an
honourable end . . .

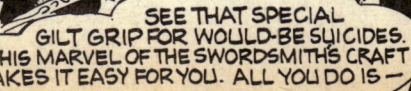

RIGHT GENTS, WHAT HAPPENED?

I WISHED TO BUY SAMURAI SWORD FOR SUICIDE ATTEMPT. THIS LOBBER WAS DEMONSTLATING WEAPON

G85

POOR DEVIL'S STILL ALIVE. IS HE GASPING OUT A LAST MESSAGE FOR HIS FAMILY?

QUIET PLEASE... HE SAYS YOU CAN HAVE THE SWORD FOR £14.10.0.

G86

GOSH BARON, I THINK WE OWE IT TO HIM TO BUY THE SWORD. £14.10.0. SEEMS REASONABLE AND HE'S GONE TO A LOT OF TROUBLE!

FRACKETT'S CURIOS

HE'S GOT A POINT, SIR...

... ON THE OTHER HAND I DON'T THINK I'D PAY THAT MUCH FOR A USED ARTICLE WITH ONE CARELESS OWNER!

Later, at the hospital . . .

But in Liverpool Sir Jos too is dicing with mortality . . .

And in the scousemakers' cellar . . .

While Sir Jos returns home, the Baron's search for death goes on . . .

And Albert goes sorrowfully
back to his anxious family . . .

And some hours later

The extraordinary legal battle reaches the court room . . .

WE CAN'T GET WORK AS A DRAG ACT, M'LUD, SINCE USING ABRASIVE COSMETIC TRIPE FROM FOSDYKES.

EXHIBIT ONE, M'LUD.

WE WERE THE TOP ACT IN ENGLAND AND NOW WE'RE RUINED, AREN'T WE ARTHUR OR MABEL?

SOB!

THERE, THERE LUV. DON'T CRY!

G105

I WILL NOT HAVE COURTROOM ATTENDANTS MAKING COMMENTS. REMOVE THAT POLICE SERGEANT!

I DON'T CARE. I'VE ALWAYS WANTED TO BE A POLICEWOMAN!

HOW DO YOU THINK THE CASE IS GOING, MR. DITCHLEY?

SHUT UP! OUR WITNESSES ARE BEING CALLED.

WOULD YOU SAY THAT THE USE OF COSMETIC TRIPE HAS IMPAIRED OR BLEMISHED THE APPEARANCE OF THE DRAG ACT HAGERTY?

MOST DEFINITELY, SIR. THEY WERE THE RAGE OF GARBIDGE STREET. WE ALL USED TO WHISTLE AFTER THEM AND SHOUT 'HELLO, SAILOR.'

...AND WHAT DO YOU DO NOW?

WE GO AND WATCH MANCHESTER UNITED.

G106

And back in the Fosdyke home . . .

As the trial continues . . .

One tension-packed hour later . . .

G.112

Panel 1:
ORDER! NOW THAT THE PLAINTIFFS HAVE FINISHED THEIR TANTALIZING STRIP WILL THEY DRESS AND I'LL PASS JUDGEMENT. PAY ATTENTION!

I'LL BASH YOUR BLEEDIN' FACE IN, DITCHLEY!

Panel 2:
OH TO HELL WITH EVERYONE...

...CASE DISMISSED!

Home once more, the Fosdykes face a new and sinister threat . . .

Panel 3:
FORGET ABOUT COSMETIC TRIPE FOR A MOMENT, LADS. GIVE ME YOUR OPINION ON THIS.

A GOOD SLAB OF FOSDYKE'S BEST. LOVELY TEXTURE!

Panel 4:
ANYONE ELSE, ALBERT?

BY THE SLASHMARKS I'D SAY IT WAS CUT AT SALFORD — *SNIFF SNIFF* - ABOUT 3·30 LAST MONDAY BY EITHER SAM WRIGGLEY OR —

Panel 5:
TASTE?

MAGNIFICENT. OUR USUAL HIGH STANDARD, DAD.

THAT IS **NOT** FOSDYKE TRIPE!

G.113

NOT FOSDYKE TRIPE, DAD? YOU MUST BE DREAMING.

G114

THERE'S A SLIGHT DIFFERENCE IN TASTE. CAN'T PUT ME FINGER ON IT, DAMMIT.'

TASTES NORMAL TO ME, TOM. DO YOU THINK HIS MIND'S GOING?

I'M WORRIED, TIM. THE WHELK AND JELLIED EEL FIASCO, THE SCOUSE DISASTER AND THEN THE COSMETIC TRIPE FARCE...

.. MUST HAVE DESTROYED HIS CONFIDENCE. I THINK HE'S GOT A PERSECUTION MANIA.'

SO...THEY'RE ALL AGAINST ME!

AM I GOING MAD? HAVE MY RECENT FAILURES SAPPED MY OLD VIGOUR..?

NO! I'M AS HARD AS I EVER WAS!

AND NOWT'LL CONVINCE ME THAT **THAT** IS FOSDYKE'S TRIPE

JOS, YOU'RE SHOUTIN' AT YOUR DINNER AGAIN.'

BY GUM, I'VE GOT IT. SCIENTIFIC ANALYSIS!

HUMOUR HIM, TIM. FETCH CHIEF CHEMIST.

RUBBISH. WHERE'S WORKS CAT?

G115

G116

G117

Can the Fosdykes overthrow this hidden oriental menace? Has the mighty tripe empire met its Waterloo?

Wait for Volume Three
or read the strip every day in THE DAILY MIRROR